Outdoor

selected by Wendy Body

Contents

Out in the dark and daylight

Out in the dark and daylight,
under a cloud or tree

Out in the park and play light,
out where the wind blows free,

Out in the March or May light
with shadows and stars to see,

Out in the dark and daylight ...
... that's where I like to be.

Aileen Fisher

Sunflakes

If sunlight fell like snowflakes,
gleaming yellow and so bright,
we could build a sunman,
we could have a sunball fight,
we could watch the sunflakes
drifting in the sky.
We could go sleighing
in the middle of July
through sundrifts and sunbanks,
we could ride a sunmobile,
and we could touch sunflakes –
I wonder how they'd feel.

Frank Asch

There are big waves

There are big waves and little waves,
Green waves and blue.
Waves you can jump over,
Waves you dive through,
Waves that rise up
Like a great water wall,
Waves that swell softly
And don't break at all...

Eleanor Farjeon

The Daffodils

I wandered lonely as a cloud
That floats on high o'er vales
    and hills,
When all at once I saw a crowd,
A host, of golden daffodils;
Beside the lake, beneath the trees,
Fluttering and dancing in the
    breeze.

William Wordsworth

The Wind

I can get through a doorway
without any key,
And strip the leaves
from the great oak tree.

I can drive storm-clouds
and shake tall towers,
Or steal through a garden
and not wake the flowers.

Seas I can move
  and ships I can sink;
I can carry a house-top
  or the scent of a pink.

When I am angry
  I can rave and riot;
And when I am spent,
  I lie quiet as quiet.

James Reeves.

The Leaves

The leaves had a wonderful frolic,
They danced to the wind's
loud song,
They whirled, and they floated,
and scampered,
They circled and flew along.

The moon saw the little
leaves dancing,
Each looked like a small
brown bird.

The man in the moon smiled
and listened,
And this is the song he heard.

The north wind is calling, is calling,
And we must whirl round
and round.
And then when our dancing
is ended
We'll make a warm quilt for
the ground.

Anonymous

Winter morning

Winter is the king of showmen,
Turning tree stumps into snow men
And houses into birthday cakes
And spreading sugar over the lakes.
Smooth and clean and frost white
The world looks good enough
    to bite.
That's the season to be young,
Catching snowflakes on
    your tongue.

Snow is snowy when it's snowing
I'm sorry it's slushy when it's going.

Ogden Nash

Robin's song

Robin sang sweetly
When the days were bright.
"Thanks! Thanks for Summer!"
He sang with all his might.

Robin sang sweetly
In the Autumn days:
"There are fruits for everyone.
Let us all give praise!"

In the cold and wintry weather
Still you hear his song.
"Somebody must sing," said Robin,
"Or Winter will seem long."

When the Spring came back again,
He sang, "I told you so!
Keep on singing through the Winter;
It will always go."

Anonymous

Pippa's song

The year's at the spring,
And day's at the morn;
Morning's at seven;
The hill-side's dew-pearled;
The lark's on the wing;
The snail's on the thorn:
God's in his heaven –
All's right with the world!

Robert Browning